INDOOR

OTHER TITLES OF INTEREST

25 SIMPLE

INDOOR AND WINDOW AERIALS

by
E. M. NOLL

BERNARD BABANI (publishing) LTD
THE GRAMPIANS
SHEPHERDS BUSH ROAD
LONDON W6 7NF
ENGLAND

© 1984 BERNARD BABANI (publishing) LTD

First Published — June 1984
Reprinted — February 1989
Reprinted — March 1992

British Library Cataloguing in Publication Data
Noll, Edward M.
        25 simple indoor and window aerials. – (BP136)
        1. Antennas(Electronics) – Amateurs' manuals
        I. Title
        621.38'028'3   TK9956
        ISBN 0 85934 111 9

Printed and Bound in Great Britain by Cox & Wyman Ltd, Reading

ABOUT THE AUTHOR

Ed Noll is an established American technical author who has written many books, articles and instruction manuals as well as having lectured and taught radio communication at various universities in the U.S.A.

He has worked on the staff of a number of broadcasting stations and as a consulting engineer.

CONTENTS

SAFETY

The safety of an installation is your responsibility when erecting an indoor or window aerial. The hazards are electrical shock, injury to a person or damage to property. Be thoughtful and wise. Do not erect an aerial where it can come in contact with electrical wires while you are making the installation or if it breaks loose from wind damage or fatigue after you have made the installation. Erect your aerial carefully so it cannot fall upon an individual or damage property during or after erection. As an extra safety precaution insulated wire is recommended.

PERSPECTIVE

Your aerial is the sensor that is activated by radio signals reaching your location from all parts of the world. Modern shortwave receivers are so sensitive that built-in, indoor and window aerials derive adequate signals from many of the high-powered radio broadcast stations. Under good propagation conditions even weaker signals are quite readable.

Many dwell in one-room studios, apartments, condominiums or other locations where outdoor aerials are prohibited. This does not mean you must forego short-wave listening. Even a 20-foot length of hook-up wire stretched out along the skirting board of a room produces acceptable results. Some additional effort and experimentation can improve performance. Strive for the combination that best meets your reception aims.

A good aerial is important in receiving weak broadcast signals particularly when you are trying to make a positive identification. If you are interested in receiving the very best signal from both strong and weak incoming signals, the aerial is important in minimizing the ill effects of fast fading, background interference and selective fading (distortion that results from some frequencies that comprise an incoming signal fading in and out relative to others). For example, a solid locked-in signal is preferred by the avid music fan. A good aerial can aid in the minimization of signal-generated (QRM) and static (QRN) interferences. More than one station may occupy the same frequency or a signal from an adjacent channel may be especially strong, producing objectionable interference. Often a directional aerial is helpful in emphasizing a desired signal and attenuating an undesired one. Fortunately good indoor and window aerials can be installed. This book tells the story.

A series of 25 indoor aerials are covered. However, it is helpful if you start by reading the Perspective and the discussions about the first ten aerial types presented. Many of the principles, ideas and construction procedures can be used again in the planning of aerials that follow.

You may wish to check and compare two or more indoor aerials to find one best suited to your needs and location. To compare one aerial to another, do so directly using a coaxial switch or some other means of making a fast changeover. You can not make an accurate comparison by taking one aerial down and replacing it with another because of the rapidity of propagation changes.

Short-Wave Bands
The official ITU short-wave bands are listed in Table 1. The 22 metre band is the latest one. The 90 and 120 metre bands are usually considered short-wave bands, however, technically it is more appropriate to consider them as medium wave frequencies. This book will introduce several aerials for use on these two bands. It should be stressed that short-wave broadcast stations cannot only be found within the frequency limits of the official bands. A host of stations operate above and below the frequency limits and, to a limited extent, on other more widely separated frequencies. Some are pirate stations and not officially allocated by their countries.

Table 1   ITU Short-wave Bands

Band (metres)	Frequency (MHz)	Band (metres)	Frequency (MHz)
120	2.3 − 2.498	25	11.65 − 12.05
90	3.2 − 3.4	22	13.6 − 13.8
75	3.95 − 4.0	19	15.1 − 15.6
60	4.75 − 5.06	16	17.55 − 17.9
49	5.95 − 6.2	13	21.45 − 21.85
41	7.1 − 7.3	11	25.67 − 26.1
31	9.5 − 9.9		

Aerial Directivity
Several indoor aerials for attic mounting have directional characteristics. In erecting a directional aerial it is important that you know the compass bearings of your particular erection site. An accurate compass is a big help. The second bit of information that you must know is the particular angles

(azimuth) of the stations to be received from your site. Fortunately, most aerials that you would use for short-wave broadcast listening have a wide selectivity response and orientation is not especially critical. Nevertheless you can do some favouring that can be helpful.

Some typical receive angles from the capital cities of London, England; Ottawa, Canada; Canberra, Australia; Wellington, New Zealand and Washington, D.C., U.S.A. to eleven countries are given in Table 2. Most of the countries selected transmit at high power on several of the short-wave bands. Such stations can be of help in checking and comparing aerials. Reception angles, mileage figures and a variety of data for more than 200 short-wave stations for your particular location may be obtained at low cost from Process Analysis Corp., 22nd Avenue, NW, Seattle, Washington, 98177, U.S.A.

If you plan to do a considerable amount of listening and aerial testing, a copy of the World Radio TV Handbook (WRTH) is very helpful. It can be purchased in almost any country of the world that has sales outlets for short-wave broadcast receiving equipment. Frequencies, schedules, powers and a vast amount of additional information are included.

Time Standard Stations

In addition to high-powered broadcast stations there are a variety of stations that transmit time and frequency standard signals. Some of these stations are in, or adjacent to, several short-wave broadcast bands. Table 3 is a partial listing. Many of these stations are on the air continuously and can be easily identified. They are excellent for making aerial comparisons.

Time Zones

Another factor in making aerial checks and matching test time with the schedule of an overseas broadcast transmission is an understanding of time zones. The International Telecommunications Union has established universal time coordinated (UTC) zone based on a 24-hour clock, 0000 to 2400. This is the same as the long-used Greenwich Mean Time (GMT). Broadcast station schedules and short-wave listening newsletters and magazines use this universal time. It is your respon-

Table 2   Typical Azimuth Angles to Sample Locations

Country/Town	Azimuth Angles From				
	London	Ottawa	Canberra	Wellington	Washington D.C.
Australia, Melbourne	74	268	–	268	257
Canada, Sackville	288	–	56	63	49
New Zealand, Wellington	20	248	113	–	243
England, London	–	53	315	342	49
USA, Washington D.C.	287	175	70	68	–
Brazil, Brasilia	226	150	159	135	147
China, Beijing	45	350	335	318	349
Germany, Cologne	95	52	312	324	44
Japan, Tokyo	31	331	352	332	330
Spain, Madrid	193	68	290	225	63
South Africa, Johannesburg	154	100	230	210	103
USSR, Moscow	64	34	316	312	32

4

Table 3
Aerial-checking Standard Time and Frequency Stations

USA Fort Collins, Colorado (WWV)
2.5MHz − 5MHz − 10MHz − 15MHz − 20MHz
(continuous)

USA Kauai, Hawaii (WWVH)
2.5MHz − 5MHz −10MHz − 15 MHz
(continuous)

CANADA Ottawa, Ontario (CHU)
3.33MHz − 7.335MHz −14.67MHz
(continuous)

AUSTRALIA Lyndhurst, Victoria (VNG)
4.5MHz   0945−2130 UTC
7.5MHz   2245−2230 UTC
12MHz   2145−0930 UTC

USSR Moscow (RWM)
4.996MHz − 9.996MHz − 14.996MHz

sibility to make the necessary conversion to local time. No such conversion is required for the United Kingdom except to add one hour during summer. Canada has six time zones. The number of hours to be subtracted from the UTC time is given in Table 4. Similar relations exist for the United States of America with the exception that the U.S.A. has only four time zones. As an example, when it is 12 noon (1200 UTC) in London, it is five hours earlier in Washington, D.C. (1200 − 500) or 7 am. Time is advanced one hour for daylight time in each zone. New Zealand has only one time zone which is ahead of UTC by 12 hours. Midnight in London is noon in New Zealand. Australia has four time zones.

Aerial Chart
A dimension chart such as that given in Table 5 provides quick answers in your design of a receiving aerial. Values are given for each band from 11 to 120 metres. The design frequency for each band is also given. Except for highly directional aerials,

Table 4   Universal Time and Time Zones

CANADIAN TIME ZONES

UTC	NEWFOUNDLAND	ATLANTIC	EST	CST	MST	PST
0000M	2030	8.30 PM	8 PM	6 PM	5 PM	4 PM
0100	2130	9.30	9	7	6	5
0200	2230	10.30	10	8	7	6
0300	2330	11.30	11	9	8	7
0400	0030	12.30	12 M	10	9	8
0500	0130	1.30 AM	1 AM	11	10	9
0600	0230	2.30	2	12 M	11	10
0700	0330	3.30	3	1 AM	12 M	11
0800	0430	4.30	4	2	1 AM	12 M
0900	0530	5.30	5	3	2	1 AM
1000	0630	6.30	6	4	3	2
1100	0730	7.30	7	5	4	3
1200N	0830	8.30	8	6	5	4
1300	0930	9.30	9	7	6	5
1400	1030	10.30	10	8	7	6
1500	1130	11.30	11	9	8	7
1600	1230	12.30 PM	12 N	10	9	8

		1.30 PM	1 PM	12 N	11AM	10 AM	9 AM
1700	1330	1 PM	12 N	11AM	10 AM	9 AM
1800	1430	2	1 PM	12 N	11	10
1900	1530	3	2	1 PM	12 N	11
2000	1630	4	3	2	1 PM	12 N
2100	1730	5	4	3	2	1 PM
2200	1830	6	5	4	3	2
2300	1930	7	6	5	4	3
2400	2030	8	7	6	5	4

USA TIME ZONES

UTC	EST	EST	EDT	CST	MST	PST
0000M	1900	7 PM	8 PM	6 PM	5 PM	4 PM
0100	2000	8	9	7	6	5
0200	2100	9	10	8	7	6
0300	2200	10	11	9	8	7
0400	2300	11	12 M	10	9	8
0500	2400	12 M	1 AM	11	10	9
0600	0100	1 AM	2	12 M	11	10

USA TIME ZONES (continued)

UTC	EST	EST	EDT	CST	MST	PST
0700	0200	2 AM	3 AM	1 AM	12 M	11 PM
0800	0300	3	4	2	1 AM	12 M
0900	0400	4	5	3	2	1 AM
1000	0500	5	6	4	3	2
1100	0600	6	7	5	4	3
1200N	0700	7	8	6	5	4
1300	0800	8	9	7	6	5
1400	0900	9	10	8	7	6
1500	1000	10	11	9	8	7
1600	1100	11	12 N	10	9	8
1700	1200	12 N	1 PM	11	10	9
1800	1300	1 PM	2	12 N	11	10
1900	1400	2	3	1 PM	12 N	11
2000	1500	3	4	2	1 PM	12 N
2100	1600	4	5	3	2	1 PM
2200	1700	5	6	4	3	2
2300	1800	6	7	5	4	3
2400	1900	7	8	6	5	4

AUSTRALIAN TIME ZONE

UTC	VICT	VICT	NA–SA	WA
0000M	1000	10 AM	9.30 AM	8 AM
0100	1100	11	10.30	9
0200	1200 N	12 N	11.30	10
0300	1300	1 PM	12.30 PM	11
0400	1400	2	1.30	12 N
0500	1500	3	2.30	1 PM
0600	1600	4	3.30	2
0700	1700	5	4.30	3
0800	1800	6	5.30	4
0900	1900	7	6.30	5
1000	2000	8	7.30	6
1100	2100	9	8.30	7
1200 N	2200	10	9.30	8
1300	2300	11	10.30	9
1400	2400M	12 M	11.30	10
1500	0100	1 AM	12.30 AM	11
1600	0200	2	1.30	12 M
1700	0300	3	2.30	1 AM

AUSTRALIAN TIME ZONE (continued)

UTC	VICT	VICT	NA–SA	WA
1800	0400	4 AM	3.30 AM	2 AM
1900	0500	5	4.30	3
2000	0600	6	5.30	4
2100	0700	7	6.30	5
2200	0800	8	7.30	6
2300	0900	9	8.30	7
2400	1000	10	9.30	8

NEW ZEALAND TIME ZONE

UTC		
0000M	1200 N	12 N
0100	1300 PM	1 PM
0200	1400	2
0300	1500	3
0400	1600	4
0500	1700	5

0600	1800	6
0700	1900	7
0800	2000	8
0900	2100	9
1000	2200	10
1100	2300	11
1200N	2400 M	12 M
1300	0100 AM	1 AM
1400	0200	2
1500	0300	3
1600	0400	4
1700	0500	5
1800	0600	6
1900	0700	7
2000	0800	8
2100	0900	9
2200	1000	10
2300	1100	11
2400	1200 N	12 N

Table 5. Dimensions, Spacings and Lengths

Band	Frequency	1 λ	2 ½λ	3 ¼λ	4 0.1λ	5 0.15λ	6 0.2λ	7 ¼λ	8 ¾λ	9 Refl.	10 Dir.
Metres	MHz	ft.	ft.	ft.	ft.	ft.	ft.	ft.	ft.	ft.	ft.
120	2.4	410	205	103	41	62	82	98	296	205	180
90	3.3	298	149	75	30	45	60	71	215	149	132
75	4.0	246	123	62	25	37	49	59	178	123	113
60	5.0	197	98	49	20	30	40	47	142	98	89
49	6.0	164	82	41	16	25	33	39	118	82	73
41	7.2	137	68	34	14	20	27	33	98	68	62
31	9.7	101	51	25	10	15	20	24	73	51	45
25	12.0	82	41	21	8	12	16	20	59	41	37
22	13.7	72	36	18	7	11	14	17	52	36	32.5
19	15.3	64	32	16	6	10	12	15.5	46	32	29
16	17.7	55	28	14	5.5	8.5	11	13.5	40	28	25
13	21.6	46	23	11.5	5	7	9	11	33	23	20.5
11	26.0	38	19	9.5	4	5.5	7.5	9	27	19	17

lengths are relatively non-critical and little difference in performance is obtained when lengths depart as much as 15–20 per cent. However, for directional aerials using parasitic reflectors and directors, use a tolerance no greater than 3 per cent. Columns 1–3 give the free-space dimensions of a wavelength, half-wavelength and quarter-wavelength. Columns 4–6 are useful in spacing phased aerials and parasitic aerial elements. Columns 7 and 8 show the dimensions for each quarter-wave side of a dipole aerial and each three-quarter wave side of a three-halves wavelength aerial. Columns 9 and 10 show lengths for parasitic reflectors and directors. Some of the longer lengths, especially for the lower-frequency bands, are not appropriate for indoor aerials but values complete the table. Equations used to calculate the various dimensions are as follows:

λ Free Space	=	$984/f_{MHz}$
$\lambda/2$ Free Space	=	$492/f_{MHz}$
$\lambda/4$ Free Space	=	$246/f_{MHz}$
0.2λ Spacing	=	$196/f_{MHz}$
0.15λ Spacing	=	$145.6/f_{MHz}$
0.1λ Spacing	=	$98.4/f_{MHz}$
$\lambda/4$ Dipole	=	$234/f_{MHz}$
$3/4\lambda$ Dipole	=	$710/f_{MHz}$
Parasitic Reflector	=	$492/f_{MHz}$
Parasitic Director	=	$450/f_{MHz}$

1. RANDOM WIRE

Don't push short-wave listening aside if you are not able to erect an outside aerial. A random length of wire can do wonders indoors, Fig.1. Use flexible insulated wire of 20 gauge SWG (18 gauge AWG) or thinner. A 20–25-foot length laid along two or three sides of a small room does well. It can be run under the carpet and/or taped to the floor along the outer perimeter of the room. If you can stretch out the 20 feet in a straight line by extending the line into the next room or along

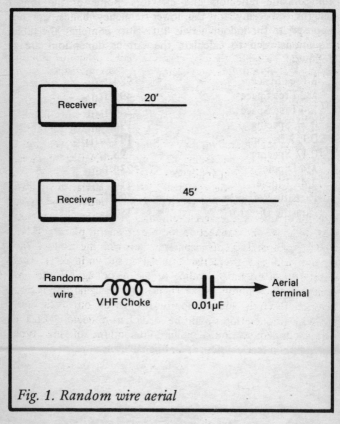

Fig. 1. Random wire aerial

a hall you can make a definite improvement in the reception of the lower frequency short-wave bands. Use a good receiver earth to plumbing or an outside earth stake.

A length of 20- 25 feet corresponds to a quarter wavelength on the 25 and 31 metre bands. If you can stretch out a 45-foot aerial over a reasonable space you can expect further improvement in low-frequency band reception. Such a length corresponds to about one-quarter wavelength on the 60 metre band.

Band-by-band reception is often inconsistent. A shift of position can often improve reception on some bands. At the same time it may cut down signal levels on other bands. A little experimentation helps if you wish to peak performance on some special band.

Another signal-boost ploy is to connect a crocodile clip on the far end of the line and clamp onto metallic surfaces. In one check the Australian stations on the 31 metre band were increased in level about 5dB simply by clamping the end of the 20-foot random length onto a large metal desk. Results can often be improved by clamping on to heating or plumbing pipes, as well as metal window or door sashes. However, don't end your short-wave-listening days by clamping on to wires, power mains, electrical appliances, etc.!

One connection you can make is to the aerial down-lead of your television or FM receiver. Connection can be made directly at one of the aerial terminals of the receiver. If you wish to make the connection more permanent, place a VHF/UHF choke and $0.1\mu F$ capacitor between the end of the random wire and the aerial terminal as shown in Fig.1. This insertion can minimize loading of the incoming TV and FM signals by the random wire. There may be signal interaction between receivers and an appropriate check out with both receivers in operation should be made before deciding on the permanent connection. Possible interactions of this type depend upon receiver designs and signal levels.

2. RANDOM WIRE AND TUNER

A tuner is especially useful in receiving the low-frequency short-wave bands when using a short aerial, as is usually required for an indoor installation, Fig.2. Three common tuner circuits are shown. Example (b) consists of a single-tapped coil and variable capacitor. The Pi-net of (c) is the most popular, presenting a lower impedance path for the resonant signal and rejecting off-frequency signals more effectively. The T-net of (d) is especially effective but has the disadvantage of requiring 2 tapped inductors that must be switched to obtain optimum results. In tests fine results were obtained using a small radio amateur T-net tuner, (MFJ-901 VERSA tuner*). It is designed for operation from 160 to 10 metres. Good results were obtained on the SWL bands especially in boosting signals on the lower frequency SWL bands when using short indoor aerials. The inductor has 12 tapped positions. Try to find a tuner with a many-tap coil.

In general, when adjusting a tuner, the capacitors are first set to the mid-scale. Then the inductor tap is moved to a setting of maximum signal. Now the variable capacitors are tuned for peak performance. On occasion you can obtain a slightly better signal by bracketing the inductor. This means trying the inductor setting one position on each side of the previous one and retuning the capacitors. However, optimum results are usually obtained with the first procedure.

If you are an ardent short-wave listener a tuner can be of benefit in building up weak signal levels and in making difficult identifications. The disadvantage of a tuner is the additional required tuning which may not be really necessary if your interests are in receiving only the block buster signals.

3. OUT-OF-WINDOW RANDOM WIRE

Indoor reception is often more difficult in large metal-beam buildings, condominiums and apartments. The metal structure

---

*MFJ Enterprises, PO Box 494, Mississippi State, MS 39762, USA

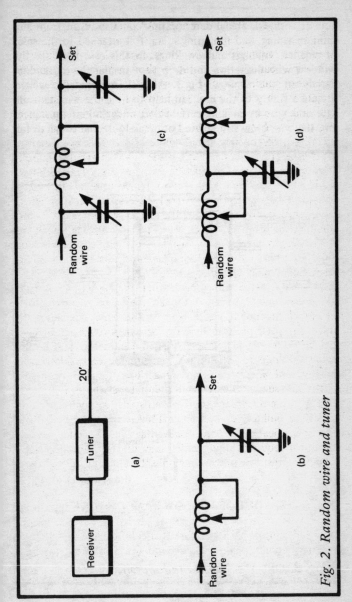

Fig. 2. Random wire and tuner

17

acts as a shield. Signal deterioration can also result from aluminium siding, and insulating metal foil attached to the sides of smaller buildings and dwellings. In this case head for the window with discretion and drop your insulated-wire random aerial out the window, Fig.3. A small non-metallic weight attached firmly to the end can help to hold the wire taut. Be safe and wise by making certain that under no circumstances can the wire blow in the wind or break loose and touch or fall

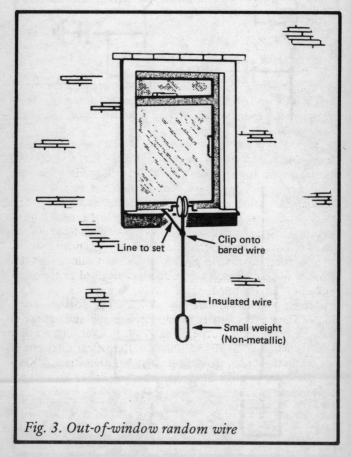

Clip onto
bared wire

Line to set

Insulated wire

Small weight
(Non-metallic)

Fig. 3. Out-of-window random wire

upon electrical wires. Use strong wire that cannot in itself break and fall. Consider your neighbour and make certain the wire does not encroach upon his domain. Use this type of aerial only where it is safe to do so. A small reel can be used to wind and unwind such an aerial.

A random wire can be wound around the window or door frame, inside or outside, to improve reception when you dwell in a shielded building. If you are lucky you may be able to clamp the random wire on to metal guttering. A metal porch railing may be accessible.

4. WINDOW WHIP

A whip aerial such as those used by radio amateurs on the 10 metre band and in some of the personal radio bands such as the 11 metre band in U.S.A. can be mounted firmly and safely on a window sill.

Such a whip can be fed in two ways. The whip itself can be simply an extension of a random-wire aerial that permits it to extend outwards away from a shielded dwelling, Fig.4. Furthermore better pick-up results. Such a whip can be fed with a coaxial line as is intended for its design application. The coaxial line will act as shielding but will have a more limited electrical length. In this case there would be a tendency for the aerial to favour the high-frequency short-wave bands. However, in a practical installation good results were obtained with this manner of feed because no ground was attached to the aerial end of the coaxial braid.

Mount your whip carefully so it cannot possibly break loose. There are a variety of mounts available such as swivel ball, swivel bracket, gutter clamp, rack bracket, etc. Choose one to match your sill and situation. Keep clear of electrical wiring. In these early paragraphs safety has been stressed. Keep these factors in mind in constructing any of the aerial types that follow.

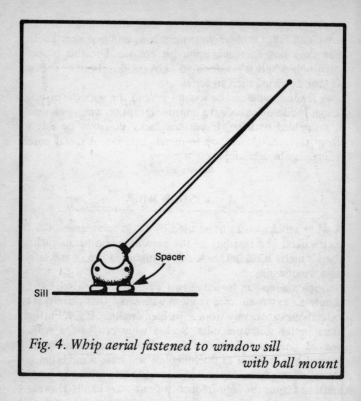

Spacer

Sill

Fig. 4. Whip aerial fastened to window sill with ball mount

5. CEILING LONG WIRE

Better performance can be obtained with a higher aerial. In as much as appearance is now always an overwhelming consideration in the radio room, a long-wire aerial with a total length that depends upon room size can be strung completely around the periphery of the room near the ceiling and, then down one wall to the receiver, Fig.5. Installed around a 12′ by 12′ room, a long-wire in excess of 50 feet is possible. Results can hold many surprises.

As mentioned previously there are quite a number of inconsistencies in the performance of an indoor aerial. Sometimes

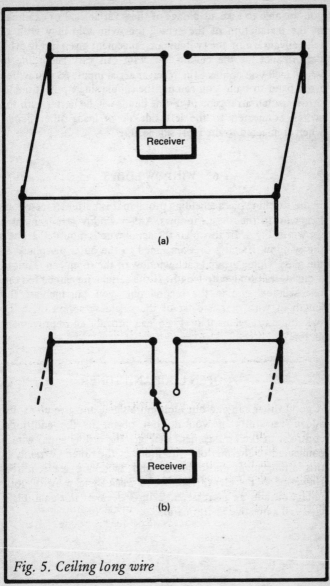

Fig. 5. Ceiling long wire

you are able to take advantage of these variables. For example, in the installation of the ceiling long-wire you may wish to take advantage of the switching arrangement given in Fig.5(b). Performance of the ceiling long-wire can vary according to which lead you connect the receiver aerial input. As you switch from band to band you can use the simple single-pole, double-throw switch arrangement. Some bands will be better with the switch connected to the left side down lead; other bands, when connected to the right side lead.

6. WINDOW LOOPS

If the dwelling has a shielding problem it is better to feed your long-wire to the room windows. A two-window arrangement is shown in Fig.6. In this plan the aerial wire is mounted around the window framing or even taped to the outer periphery of the glass. Going around each window of the room can result in a fair overall long-wire length. If the aerial wire can be fed out one window and in the second one, you can increase the length of wire that is clear of the shielding action. Also the switching arrangement of Fig.5 can provide an improvement factor.

7. OPEN-LOOP AND TUNER

A good tuner can eke out a bit more signal and give you some added versatility if you do not object to the additional controls. In the arrangement of Fig.7 the ceiling aerial wire is connected to the random-wire input of the tuner. Certainly in this arrangement more tuning and switching are required. However, in the identification of a weak signal a bit of noise reduction and an increase of 2 or 3 decibels in signal might give you a positive identification.

22

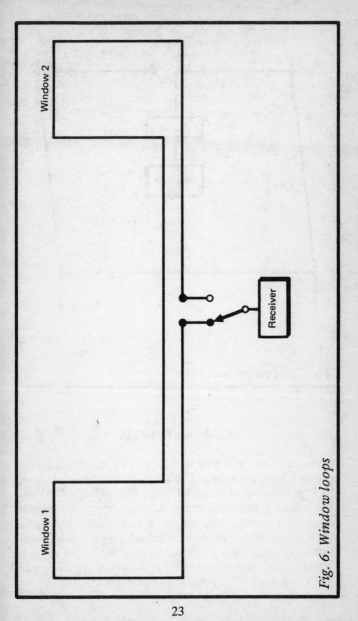

Window 1 · Window 2 · Receiver

Fig. 6. Window loops

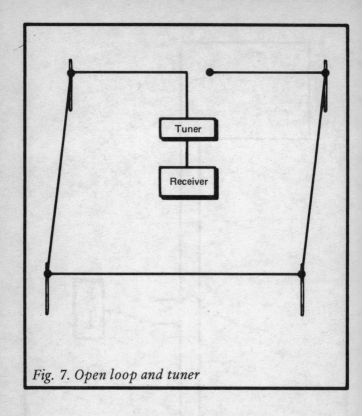

Fig. 7. Open loop and tuner

8.   WINDOW HELIX

A low-cost and effective vertical can be constructed from insulated hook-up wire and PVC (polyvinyl chloride) piping, Fig.8. A 5- or 6-foot length of 1-inch PVC piping will do well. If you have a tall window you may be able to use a longer length with a secure attachment. A swivel mounting bracket which is attached to the window sill will permit you to tilt the vertical outward away from the window. When you do so be certain to use a guy arrangement at the top of the window (or even a long bracket) to prevent whipping in the wind.

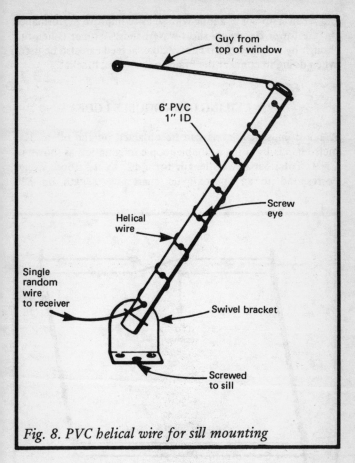

Fig. 8. *PVC helical wire for sill mounting*

Good performance on the 11 to 19 metre bands is obtained using a helical-wire length of approximately 15.5 feet which is laced through screw eyes turned into the PVC piping. Space the screw eyes to accommodate the overall length of wire you plan to use. A 15.5-foot length also resulted in acceptable performance on the 22 to 31 metre bands as well. A random-wire feed was used permitting the position of the helical wire and the wire connecting from the base to the receiver to act as a long-wire so as to improve performance on the lower frequency short-wave bands. A tuner is helpful, though by no means mandatory. Coaxial feed can also be used. When doing so connect the braid to the swivel bracket.

9. CEILING OPEN DOUBLE LOOP

A boost in signal levels can be obtained on the 60 to 120 metre bands by using a double-loop configuration as shown in Fig.9. Total aerial wire length for a 12′ by 12′ room would correspond to an approximate quarter-wavelength on 120

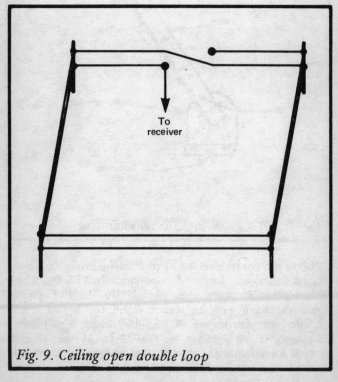

To receiver

Fig. 9. Ceiling open double loop

metres. Aerial configuration provides an acceptable all-band performance. Connect the down lead to the single- or random-wire input of the receiver. Use a good receiver earth.

To improve performance use a switchable input or tuner for the open double-loop. Refer to Figs.5 and 7.

10. ATTIC OR CRAWL-SPACE DIPOLE

The roof space or attic above a dwelling is an attractive site for aerial erection. The advantages are the high location as well as the ability to install a reasonably long aerial. Maximum height can be obtained by mounting the aerial directly beneath the apex of the roof. This position also clears the aerial of the shielding and discontinuities introduced by wiring, pipes, and metal siding, providing the roof is non-metallic. Screw eyes can be used to hold the aerial to the apex beam, Fig.10. Depending upon dwelling size the mounting can support full-length dipoles on the 19, 22 and 25 metre bands, and, perhaps, one for the 31 metre band if you have a large dwelling.

Again the aerial can be constructed of hook-up wire. The down lead can be low-cost two-wire audio cable. In a check on a dipole aerial a 60-foot length of coaxial cable was compared with a 60-foot length of 2-conductor audio cable using 26 SWG (24 AWG) speaker wire (Radio Shack 278-1509) with only an insignificant decrease in signal level even on the higher-frequency short-wave bands. The audio cable can be run under carpets and along the skirting board in a reasonably concealed manner. Dipole dimensions are given in Table 5.

11. SQUEEZE-IN DIPOLES

When mounting space is limited, effective aerial length can be added in a number of ways as shown in Fig.11. The inverted dipole of (a) is a configuration adaptable to indoor use especially for attic mounting directly beneath pitched roofs. The feed point is located at the apex beam with side legs that can be run along the side beams and down the vertical

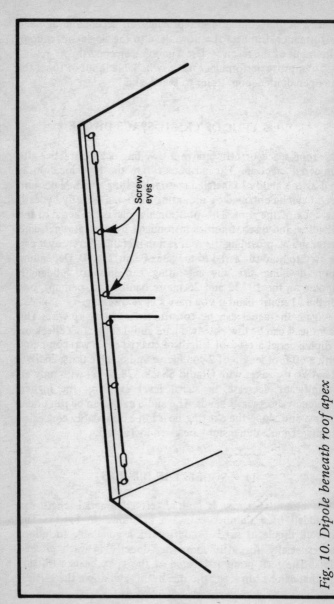

Screw eyes

Fig. 10. Dipole beneath roof apex

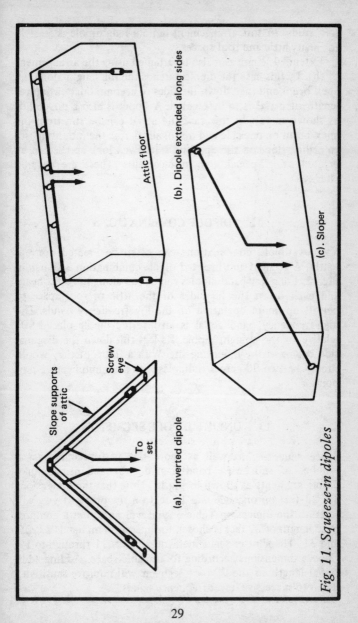

Screw eye

Slope supports
of attic

To
set

(a). Inverted dipole

Attic floor

(b). Dipole extended along sides

(c). Sloper

Fig. 11. Squeeze-in dipoles

side studs. In this arrangement quite a long dipole is feasible for many attic and roof spaces.

Extended length can also be attained using the arrangement of (b). In this case the dipole extends the full length along the apex beam and then down the sides to accommodate whatever length of aerial is to be erected. A sloper is also a possibility as shown in (c). In this case the aerial can be run from the apex beam on one side and diagonally across the mounting site to ceiling floor on the opposite side. Even long aerials can be erected using special loop arrangements. These are covered later.

12.   DIPOLE COMBINATIONS

Various dipole combinations can often be erected conveniently. A straight and inverted dipole combination is shown in Fig.12. Long low-band dipoles can be run along the apex beam and even down the far sides of the attic or roof space to permit optimum operation on the low-frequency bands. The high-frequency band aerial is an inverted dipole placed 90° relative to the straight dipole. Its legs run down the diagonal side beams of the mounting site. With a flat roof they would simply be two 90° crossed dipoles with a common centre-feed point.

13.   UNLIKE DIPOLE SEGMENTS

Space squeezing as well as more flat performance over a number of short-wave bands can be obtained using unlike dipole segments as shown in Fig.13. Note that the dimensions are 22 feet on one side and 15 feet on the other. If you will refer to the dimension Table 5, you will note that a compromise length of 22 feet is chosen for operation on bands 22, 25, and 31. The shorter segment favours bands 11 through to 19. Choose dimensions according to available space. Adding additional length to the 22-foot segment will improve sensitivity down to successive lower-frequency bands.

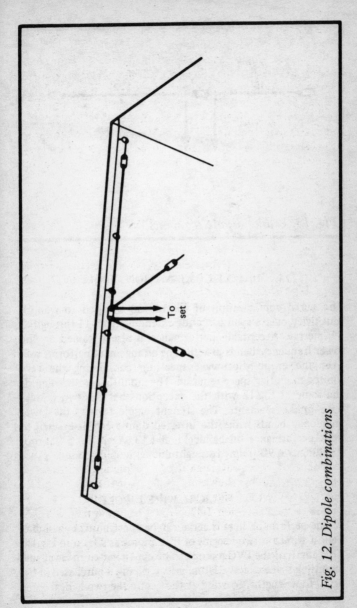

To set

Fig. 12. Dipole combinations

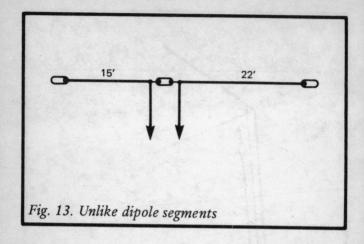

Fig. 13. Unlike dipole segments

14.   UNLIKE COMBINATION DIPOLES

The aerial configuration of Fig.14 can be used to smooth
sensitivity over a span of bands extending from 11 through to
31 metres. Acceptable performance is also obtained on the
lower-frequency bands as well. The arrangement performs well
over the entire short-wave spectrum considering the very
limited mounting space required. The mounting arrangement is
the same as Fig.12 with the exception that the two dipoles
have unlike segments. The straight dipole favours the lower
frequency bands while the inverted dipole can be erected to
peak performance on bands 11 and 13. Again for a flat-roof
dwelling two 90° related straight dipoles would be used.

15.   HELICAL WIRE DIPOLE

A fine-performing indoor aerial can be constructed by winding
helical wires on two lengths of PVC piping as shown in Fig.15.
The length of the PVC piping can be cut to match the available
mounting space exactly. Usually PVC piping is purchased in 10-
or 20-foot lengths. Starting at the centre the two helical wires

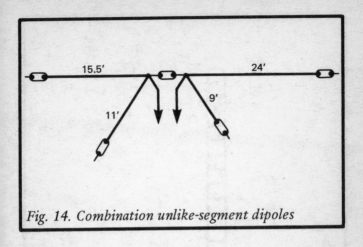

Fig. 14. Combination unlike-segment dipoles

can be wound to the ends. A second possibility is to saw the 10-foot length in half as shown in Fig.15.

PVC piping comes in various diameters that can be telescoped together. You can construct a longer aerial by purchasing two 20-foot sections choosing one with a smaller diameter so that it can be telescoped into the other and bolted into position. In a typical arrangement each would be cut in half. On each side, the small diameter segment would be telescoped two feet into the larger diameter segment. Consequently the overall length of each segment would be 18 feet and there would be a total dipole length of 36 feet.

The overall length of wire used depends upon the overall length of the PVC piping and the nearness of the helical turns. Good all-band performance results from the use of two 45-foot lengths of hook-up wire and two 18-foot PVC piping segments. Use a tapered helical wind bringing the turns nearer to each other at the aerial ends. Helical wires can be held in place with tacks or screw eyes turned into the piping. Drill a small hole to permit starting the screw eye. Full details about the construction of PVC piping outdoor aerials can be found in book number BP132: *25 Simple Shortwave Broadcast Band Aerials*, by the same author and publisher as this book.

PVC piping can be held to the apex beam with suitable

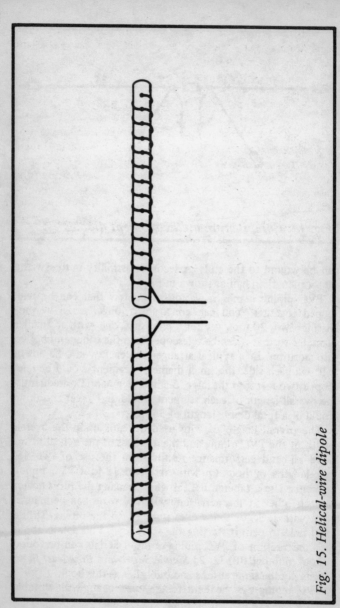

Fig. 15. Helical-wire dipole

brackets or to one of the beams of a flat-roofed construction. If more convenient it can be suspended because of its light weight. Use rope or insulated wire.

16. ATTIC TRIANGLE

If you wish to emphasize performance on a specific band or two, the triangle lends itself to mounting beneath a sloping roof as shown in Fig.16. This arrangement with a 38-foot overall length (refer to Table 5) was ideal for the reception of the Republic of South Africa signal transmitting in the 11 metre

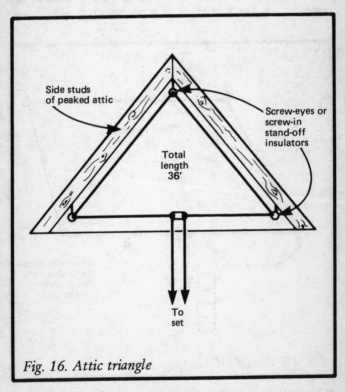

Side studs
of peaked attic

Screw-eyes or
screw-in
stand-off
insulators

Total
length
36'

To
set

Fig. 16. Attic triangle

band. Several eye-rings permit easy mounting of this configuration when screwed into the apex beam and the side studs.

17.   ATTIC CLOSED LOOPS

Full-wave loops are adaptable to indoor mounting. Configuration can be triangular squared, or rectangular. All depends on the mounting site. As shown in Fig.17 the mounting area need not be square but can be rectangular just so long as it provides the required total length. In a typical installation for a pitched roof the full-wave loop aerial is mounted horizontally in the rafters of the roof or, as in Fig.17, it can be suspended from the side studs of a pitched attic. Mount it as

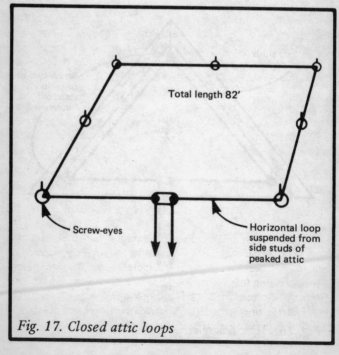

Total length 82'

Screw-eyes

Horizontal loop suspended from side studs of peaked attic

Fig. 17. Closed attic loops

high as possible but at a point that will give you the necessary space even though it may be just off the attic floor. One is surprised at just how much aerial wire you can string in such a loop mounted in a rather confined area.

At our location an 82-foot loop was fastened to the side studs of a pitched roof to check out reception of the Spanish signal on 11.88 MHz and the Australian signal on 11.80 MHz. Fine results were obtained on this 25 metre band. Good results were also obtained on the 19 and 31 metre bands. In fact, the aerial provided quite acceptable performance over the short-wave spectrum.

18.   ATTIC LONG-WIRE OPEN LOOP

The open-wire loop permits the erection of a long aerial, Fig.18. Usually space is available for a quarter-wavelength of wire on either the 75, 90 or 120 metre bands. Thus you can anticipate good reception on these low-frequency bands. The 82-foot loop of Aerial 17 when operated as a single wire performs very well as a low-frequency aerial.

Band-to-band results vary as in any long wire. In addition there are discontinuities found in indoor installations. If you wish to eke out the very best performance you may wish to use a tuner. Connect the single lead to the random wire input of the tuner. The down lead can be flexible hook-up wire that can be hidden with ease.

19.   SWITCHABLE OPEN-WIRE LOOP

An option to an aerial/tuner combination is the simple two-wire down lead and a double-throw, single-pole switch of Fig.19. For best results it is advisable to use a low-capacity two-wire down lead. Flat 300-ohm line does well. An alternative plan is to use two lengths of hook-up wire spaced between one-half and one inch. As you switch band-to-band determine which switch position provides the stronger signal.

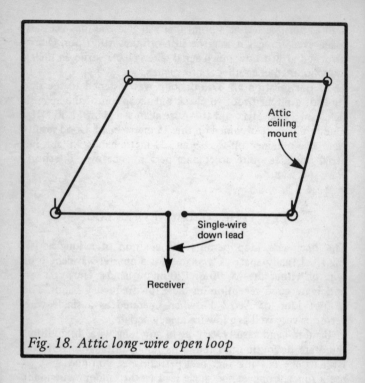

Fig. 18. Attic long-wire open loop

20. ALL-BAND O/C LOOP WITH TUNER

The ultimate loop configuration is shown in Fig.20. It provides good indoor results on all bands from 11 to 120 metres. However, it involves the use of a tuner as well as a simple double-pole, double-throw switch, Fig.20. Use 300-ohm line between the loop and the receiving position.

Choose a loop overall length according to available space and the band or two you wish to favour. Attractive lengths are 64, 82 and 101 feet which set up a full-wavelength closed loop on the 19, 25 or 31 metre bands. Excellent results are obtained on the band for which the loop is cut as well as two or three bands on each side. In this mode of operation the

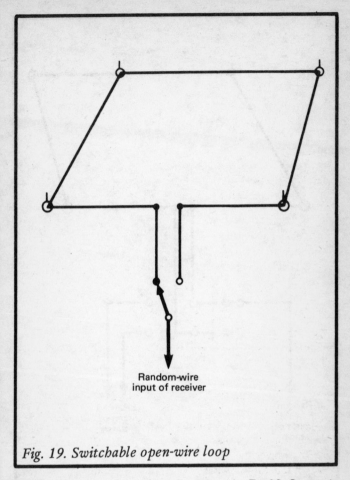

Random-wire
input of receiver

Fig. 19. Switchable open-wire loop

DPDT switch is connected to the right side, Fig.20. Output is applied to the balanced input of the tuner.

For optimum results on other bands try both positions of the switch. Usually you will find that the low frequency bands of 60 to 120 metres are better using the loop in an open fashion (switch set to the left side) and single lead applied to random-wire input of the tuner.

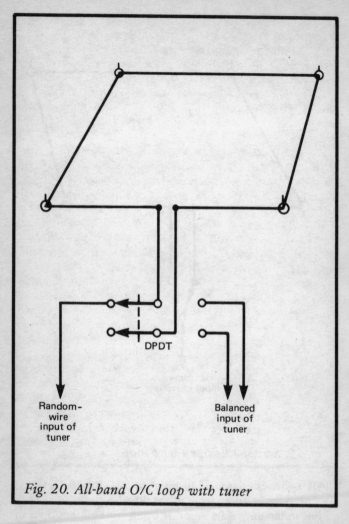

DPDT

Random-
wire
input of
tuner

Balanced
input of
tuner

Fig. 20. All-band O/C loop with tuner

If you use the aerial of Fig.20 prepare a chart that shows switch position settings, tuner coil and capacitor settings. Thus in changing bands you can quickly reset the switch and tuner to the combination that produces the best results. The tedious procedure of finding optimum results on each band need only be done once.

The installation will also provide acceptable results on frequencies lower than the 120 metre band if your tuner tunes to this range of frequencies. If the tuner does not tune this low you can bypass the tuner for the random-wire reception of lower frequencies.

21. MW BROADCAST BAND LONG-WIRE

An attic often provides adequate space for erection of a very long aerial that will improve performance on the medium-wave broadcast band extended between 550 kHz and 1600 kHz as well as the short-wave broadcast bands. Results do vary from band to band but they can be peaked on an individual band with the use of a tuner. However, results are quite acceptable without a tuner if you are not overly critical.

Such an aerial is wound in orderly fashion among the studs and beams of the attic. Our own installation was wound back and forth along both sloping sides of the roof ceiling. A continuous piece of hook-up wire was used. An optimum dimension was found to be about a quarter wavelength between 0.9 and 1 MHz (240–260 feet). This includes the length of the down lead from the attic to the receiver input. It is interesting to reflect that such an aerial would be difficult to erect exterior to your house but seems to fit quite well into a rather small attic or roof space. Layout can be square or rectangular and accommodates to the configuration of the mounting site. Do not expect the ultimate from this aerial its advantage is its good-performing all-band capability.

22. PARASITIC BEAMS

A parasitic aerial element has no direct connection with the element to which the transmission line is attached. A parasitic element reflector is cut longer than its associated dipole and resonates on a frequency lower than the connected element.

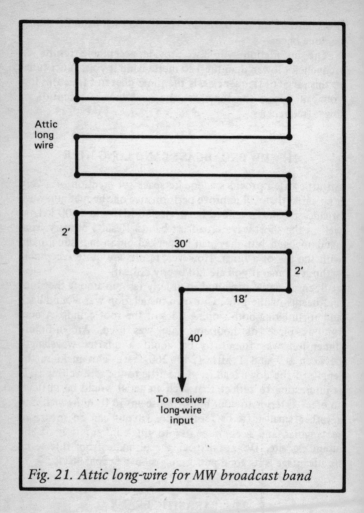

Fig. 21. Attic long-wire for MW broadcast band

Maximum directivity is broadside in a line extending from the reflector through the dipole. Parasitic director is cut shorter than the dipole. In this case, there is maximum directivity in a line between the dipole and the parasitic director. Arrangement and dimensions are given in examples (a) and (b) of

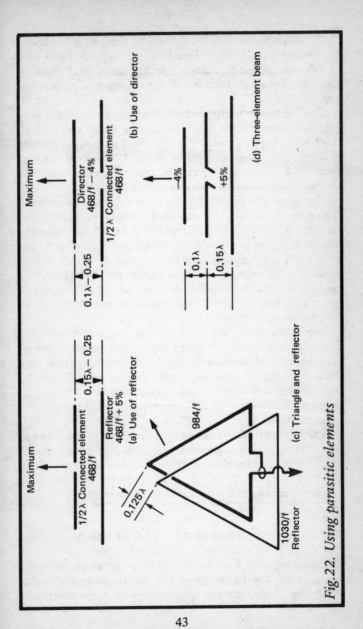

Fig. 22. Using parasitic elements

Fig.22. This information for the various short-wave bands can be obtained from Table 5. Equations are supplied if you wish to calculate dimensions for a specific preferred frequency. These are shown in Fig.22 and also are given in association with Table 5.

Attic beams are quite feasible depending upon mounting space available and the band or bands for which you wish to construct a beam. Beams can be fastened to the ceiling studs or suspended. They can even be fastened to the attic or roof space floor. Depending upon attic configuration you may be able to erect a beam for your favourite station(s).

The beam can be constructed of thin-diameter aluminium tubing up to the use of inexpensive television-mast tubing (1 or 1.25 inch diameter). No crossarm is required because the individual elements are individually fastened. You do not need to worry about supporting a heavy beam to a mast as you would for an external erection. Gauge 16 SWG (14 AWG) hook-up wire can be attached to thin-diameter PVC piping to serve as a beam element. Also hook-up wire itself can be fastened to studs or floor using wire staples.

Depending upon the attic configuration and operating frequency the spacing between dipole and parasitic can be close or wide. More often than not close-spacing must be used because of limited mounting space. Coaxial or 300-ohm flat line can link the beam to the receiving position. Our preference has been the use of 300-ohm flat line and a tuner with a balanced input.

The triangle aerial of example (c) shows how a reflector can be added to a triangle element such as that detailed in Aerial 16. The basic three-element beam is shown in example (d). Elements are close-spaced although, if space is available, they can be separated as much as one-quarter wavelength.

23. PRACTICAL ATTIC BEAMS

The examples of Fig.23 show that attic beams are quite practical on the higher frequency shortwave bands. A 25-metre dipole and director combination requires about an 8

44

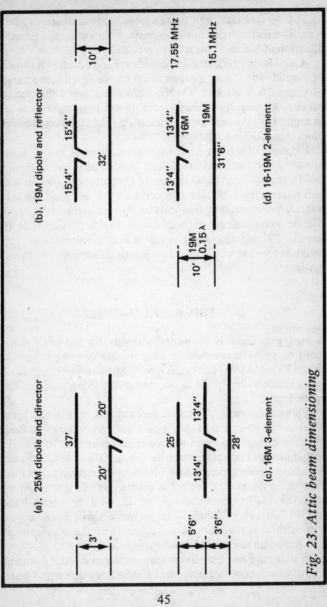

Fig. 23. Attic beam dimensioning

(a). 25M dipole and director

(b). 19M dipole and reflector

(c).16M 3-element

(d) 16-19M 2-element

45

feet by 40 feet area. The two-element beam is rather long but critical orientation is not necessary. Point it in the general direction of the area you wish to receive.

A dipole and reflector combination for 19 metres is shown in example (b). Note that this beam can be fitted into an area of about 10 × 32 feet. On the highest-frequency short-wave bands you may have space for a three-element beam as in example (c). You are now considering a 28 × 14 square feet mounting area.

Example (d) shows how a two-element beam can be compromised for two-band reception. The aerial is cut to favour the 16 metre band. However, using a rather long reflector will also provide some limited gain on the 19 metre band. Thus if your favourite station transmits on two adjacent bands there will be some peaking on both bands. Use the information in Aerials 22 and 23 along with the dimension chart and equations to come up with a combination that might suit your needs.

24.   THIN-WIRE LONG WIRES

A long-wire aerial is not an impossibility for the small apartment or single-room dweller with the use of magnet wire of gauge 26 or 28 SWG (24 or 26 AWG). Such an aerial is feasible for a receiver that must be located in the living room of the apartment.

Thin-wire is easily hidden. Two examples of thin-wire long-wires are given in Fig.24. Such an aerial can be taped to floor under a carpet. An open double loop beneath a 10′ by 10′ carpet provides adequate space for a quarter wavelength on the 90 metre band (approximately 70 feet) The ladder construction of example (b) can set a quarter wavelength aerial up into the higher-frequency half of the AM broadcast band (550–1600 kHz). To eke out the most signal possible you may wish to use a tuner. A good ground on the receiver helps in building up the lower frequency signals.

If you have more available space you can stretch the same length of wire over a greater area and be rewarded with higher-

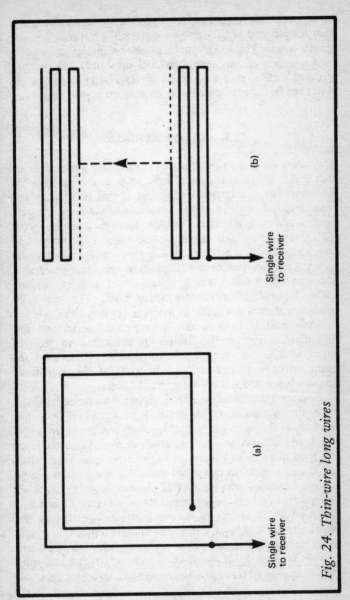

Single wire
to receiver

(a)

Single wire
to receiver

(b)

Fig. 24. Thin-wire long wires

signal levels. In a larger apartment you may be able to keep the wire hidden and at the same time stretch it out over a much greater length. This too improves received signal levels.

A number of the aerials covered previously can be constructed with magnet wire if you prefer a well hidden system. Wires can be fastened down with transparent plastic tape.

25.   ACTIVE AERIALS

The active aerial incorporates a short aerial and a pre-amplifier that comes ahead of the aerial input of your receiver, Fig.25. The amplifier is a low-noise unit and is able to build up the weak received signal to a level acceptable to the receiver input. Such a system is attractive for older receivers and those with limited sensitivity and signal-to-noise ratio. Improvement is only marginal for a modern top-line receiver. The active aerial is attractive for indoor use, depending upon receiver design and can often match the performance of a short outdoor aerial, especially on lower-frequency bands. The two basic types are shown in Fig.25. In example (a) the active aerial is a single unit affair including a very short aerial and the amplifier/control facility. Output is connected to receiver input with a short length of coaxial cable. These units are quite effective in building up the levels of the short-wave tropical bands and AM broadcast band signals.

A more versatile and better-performing active aerial is the type that separates the aerial and its amplifier from the controls as shown in example (b). Aerial and amplifier can be mounted outdoors on window, porch or roof. The aerial itself is a yard or so in length and acts as a better signal sensor than the short aerial of an integrated unit. The aerial could also be mounted indoors near the roof of the dwelling. The amplifier and control unit can be separated by as much as 50 feet. The fact that the amplifier is remote positioned relative to the aerial proper improves the signal-to-noise ratio. The single cable interchanges signal and supply voltages for the amplifier.

Checks with a MFJ–1024* remote active antenna were

---

*MFJ Enterprises, PO Box 494, Mississippi State, MS 37962, USA

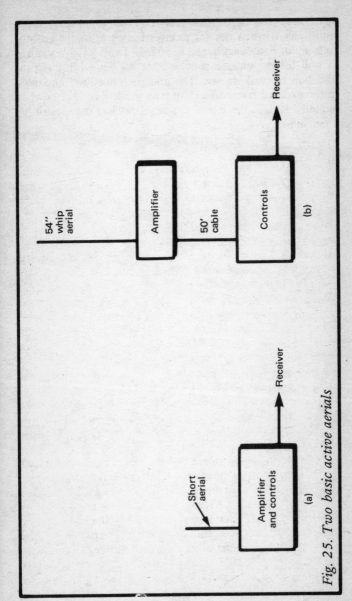

Fig. 25. Two basic active aerials

54" whip aerial

Amplifier

50' cable

Controls

→ Receiver

(b)

Short aerial

Amplifier and controls

→ Receiver

(a)

impressive using a top-line receiver. You can expect more improvement when using a receiver having a lower signal-to-noise ratio. Frequency range is 50 kHz to 30 MHz. If you are an avid listener such an aerial system is a big aid in the identification of weak signals. The unit performed well mounted to the external frame of a floor-level window and better when mounted so that the top of the aerial reached the apex of the attic ceiling.

ALSO OF INTEREST

BP105: AERIAL PROJECTS
R. A. Penfold

Whether you have built a very simple short-wave receiver or have purchased a most sophisticated piece of equipment, the performance you achieve will ultimately depend on the aerial to which your set is connected.

The subject of aerials is vast but in this book the author has considered practical aerial designs, including active, loop and ferrite aerials which give good performances and are relatively simple and inexpensive to build. The complex theory and mathematics of aerial design have been avoided.

Also included are constructional details of a number of aerial accessories including a preselector, attenuator, filters and tuning unit.

96 pages   *1982*
0 85934 080 5   **£1.95**

BP91: AN INTRODUCTION TO RADIO DXING
R. A. Penfold

There is a strange fascination in being able to listen in your own living room to a broadcast, be it commercial or by a radio amateur, which is being transmitted from a location many thousands of miles away, possibly across the other side of the world.

Anyone can switch on a short-wave receiver and play with the controls until they pick up something, but to find a particular station, country or type of broadcast and to receive it as clearly as possible with the minimum of distortion and interference requires a little more skill and knowledge. The object of this book is to help the reader do just that, which in essence is the fascinating hobby of radio DXing.

The book is divided into two main sections, one devoted to amateur band reception and the other covering broadcast band reception, with advice on suitable equipment and the techniques employed when using the equipment. Also, for those interested in actually building projects, the construction of a number of useful accessories are described.

112 pages   *1981*
0 85934 066 X   **£1.95**

Please note following is a list of other titles that are available in our range of Radio, Electronics and Computer Books.

These should be available from all good Booksellers, Radio Component Dealers and Mail Order Companies.

However, should you experience difficulty in obtaining any title in your area, then please write directly to the publisher enclosing payment to cover the cost of the book plus adequate postage.

If you would like a complete catalogue of our entire range of Radio, Electronics and Computer Books then please send a Stamped Addressed Envelope to:

BERNARD BABANI (publishing) LTD
THE GRAMPIANS
SHEPHERDS BUSH ROAD
LONDON W6 7NF
ENGLAND